Can You Hear Me?

Hope After Loss

Y.Y. Chan

Published by Chan Yee Yue Irenee

Cover Design by 100Covers.com
Interior Design by FormattedBooks.com

ISBN: 978-988-74652-1-8 (Paperback)
ISBN: 978-988-74652-0-1 (Hardback)
ISBN: 978-988-74652-2-5 (eBook)

Chan, Y.Y.
Can You Hear Me? / Y.Y. Chan

To my dad, Charles (1956 – 2017),
for always listening to me,
even in Heaven.
Thank you for believing in me,
even when I didn't believe in myself.

To my grandma, Ying Chong (1925 – 2020),
for teaching me how to live life tp the fullest,
despite our age.
I will miss your adorable smiles,
creative stories and beautiful singing.

With all my love,

Y. Y.

"Grief never ends, but it changes. It's a passage, not a place to stay. Grief is not a sign of weakness, nor a lack of faith. It is the price of love."

—*Unknown*

Contents

1   The News that Changed Everything

16 November 2016
5:40 p.m.

I don't know who I can talk to about what I just heard. I'm still trying to process everything and not exactly sure what to do.

When I got home after school today, Daddy was already home. Usually he comes home quite late—around seven or eight o'clock, sometimes even later, so it was strange to see him home by four. When I walked in the front door, I saw him sitting on the couch in the living room with Mummy. They held hands and had tears in their eyes. I put my school bag down and rushed over to ask what was wrong. Mummy told me to sit down. That's when Daddy told me that he is sick.

He took a day off work to see the doctor. It was already his second visit and he said that the doctors found cancer in his body. He said that he feels some pain and discomfort when he eats.

I feel bad that I hadn't noticed anything wrong before. He never told us about the pain.

He had gone to see the doctor last week and they did some blood tests and scans. Today, he went in to get the results. He didn't tell Mummy about it until he got home today, so she was surprised when he came home early too. He said he didn't want to scare us and make us worry if it turned out to be nothing, but he couldn't keep it from us now because it is quite serious.

He doesn't look very sick, though. But he said the cancer will soon spread and make his body weaker and weaker. The cancer is in his pancreas—I don't know exactly what the pancreas does, but I think it is part of the digestive system? I will look it up after dinner. I wonder what kind of treatments there are. There must be something that can help, right?

9:00 p.m.

I'm still in a bit of shock. I could barely finish my dinner. My stomach felt so uncomfortable and I almost choked on a bit of cabbage. It was like my mind was everywhere and I couldn't concentrate on eating or swallowing food. Mummy told me to go to bed early tonight. I've been sitting in my bed for an hour because I can't sleep. My mind is everywhere.

I looked up "cancer pancreas" on Google. I doubt Mummy or Daddy would tell me much about it. I read a few webpages from some medical sites and found out that the pancreas is an organ that releases enzymes that aid digestion and makes hormones to help manage blood sugar. Cancer in the pancreas starts in the tissues and can grow into tumours. Pancreatic cancer is rarely detected in the early stages (when it is most curable). And, this next part made me realise just how real and serious it is—symptoms often don't occur until it begins to spread to other organs. Daddy said he was already experiencing pain in his abdomen, which is one of the symptoms. It's already begun to spread. It's not curable. I want to scream.

It's also one of the most aggressive cancers you can get. There are not many treatment options either, since there is no cure. He could have surgery, chemotherapy, or radiation therapy, or a combination of them all. I remember when Auntie Helen had chemotherapy three years ago—she lost all of her hair and got really thin. She still passed away after nine months. I'm not really sure what type of cancer she had, though. Mummy and Daddy didn't tell me. I was really shocked when she passed away. I didn't even get to say "goodbye." I wonder if it was the same as what Daddy has now. Is that how long he has—nine months?

I feel… I don't know how I feel—is it sadness, anger, frustration, helplessness? Maybe it's all of those. The fact that this is even happening right now is crazy. It's a dream. This is not real. I'm only twelve. He's only been my dad for twelve years. What if the cancer kills him? He won't be able to see me graduate high school. What would I do without him?

Who's going to take me to concerts or go swimming with me? He won't be there when I get into university or start my first job. He won't meet any of my boyfriends or see me get married… Daddies are not supposed to get sick like this! It's not fair!

I wish I knew how to make him better. All I can think to do is pray: "Dear Heavenly Father, please heal my dad. Make him better and don't let him get any sicker. Protect him from all the bad cancer cells—no, kill all the cancer cells in his body—and give him all the best doctors and medicine to heal him. Just… give him more time. In Jesus' name, Amen."

I wonder if God can hear my prayer. Will He be mad that I only pray when something bad happens or when I want something? Daddy always reminds me to pray and thank God for everything and ask for forgiveness. I often forget, though. Is that why this is happening? Is God punishing him because of me?

I try to pray again: "Dear Heavenly Father, please forgive me that I haven't been praying much lately. I'm sorry for all the stupid things I have done, like sneaking junk food into my room, and staying up to play video games instead of doing my homework, not helping Mummy when she needs it, and skipping my lessons, and so many other terrible things I have done but can't remember right now. I've been a really bad girl lately, but please don't punish my dad because of me. He hasn't done anything wrong. He has helped a lot of people. He doesn't deserve this. Punish me instead. I'm the one who doesn't obey You and forgets to pray. I'm really sorry. Please make it stop. In Jesus' name, Amen."

2 (Possibly) Our Last Christmas Together

25 December 2016
11:30 a.m.

Even though it's Christmas today, I don't really feel like celebrating. Daddy said that it might be his last Christmas with us and that made me feel even worse. I don't know if I should be happy or sad… or… whatever.

Mummy invited some of their close friends from church and university over. Grandma, Grandpa, Uncle Mitch, and Aunt Jillian (from Daddy's side) are also coming over. They are all arriving later in the afternoon.

Mummy prepared the dishes for tonight while Daddy rested in his room. She asked me to bring Daddy some hot water. When I got to his room, I saw him sitting up on the bed, reading. He was reading a story that I wrote for him last year. It was a silly story, about us going skydiving together. Both of us are actually deathly scared of heights, but in my story, we are fearless, and we can do anything. I once told Daddy that we can be and do anything in stories, no matter how unbelievable or unrealistic it is—he really liked that.

"How come you don't write stories anymore, Renee?" he asked.

"I do sometimes, but I don't always finish them. And they're not very good."

"I'm sure that's not true. I like all the stories you write. Can you write me another story? About you and me?" he asked. "That would be a wonderful Christmas present!"

I'd already gotten Daddy a Christmas present—a new pair of headphones—but now that I think about it, it's a rather silly gift, and I think the story would be much better. I told him it might be a little late for Christmas, though. He laughed and said, "Well, as long as I can read it before *next* Christmas!" I know he was joking, but it made me wonder how much time he really has. I'd better come up with some ideas tomorrow.

8:45 p.m.

Grandma, Grandpa, and Mummy and Daddy's friends arrived around 5:00 p.m. They were in the living room drinking tea and chatting with Daddy until Uncle Mitch and Aunt Jillian arrived half an hour later.

Mummy said that we would have an early dinner so Daddy could go to bed early. I helped Mummy bring out the dishes and lay everything on the table. Everything looked so yummy. Mummy prepared a bowl just for Daddy. He cannot eat a lot of meat and can only take small bites these days. His bowl contained mostly congee with some mixed veggies and a little bit of minced chicken. Mummy mixed everything in a blender so that it was like a thick porridge. It didn't look the most appealing and probably tasted rather bland. I felt a little guilty eating the gorgeous spread on the table when he couldn't have any. But Daddy seemed quite happy anyway and smiled and laughed with his friends.

I didn't say much. I just watched and listened to their conversations. They shared some stories about when they were in university together in Canada. It was nice to see Daddy laugh and look so happy. He hadn't laughed like that in a while.

After dinner, they continued to chat for a bit while Mummy prepared the dessert. One of Daddy's friends prayed for us and Daddy. He prayed for Mummy and me to trust God no matter what happens, and to have faith that He will do what is best for Daddy. What does that mean—what is best for Daddy? Isn't what is best for him to get better? Why didn't he pray for that or for a cure? I felt a bit annoyed, so I silently prayed for it myself. I've been asking God to make Daddy better since the day he told us about the cancer, but he seems to be getting worse. I started to wonder—*Maybe I'm not praying hard enough, and not enough people are praying for it. Why aren't Daddy's friends praying for it? Don't they want him to get better? Is Daddy praying to get better himself?*

Their friends left shortly after dessert, and only Grandma, Grandpa, Uncle Mitch, and Aunt Jillian remained. We exchanged our gifts. Mummy and Daddy got me a book—*A Little Princess*. I remember watching the movie with Daddy last year, and he had told me that it was based on a book. I never got around to getting the book or reading it.

"This is for *our* little princess," Daddy said proudly. "They say the book is way better than the movie."

"They always are!" I exclaimed. "They always change something in the movie."

"Well, they definitely changed something—the ending, especially. But I won't spoil it for you," he said. I think I know what the book ending is, but I don't say anything. Movies always—well, usually—have a happy ending.

Then Mummy handed my present to Daddy. I had forgotten to take the headphones away from the gift pile this morning after Daddy said he wanted me to write him a story. I told him that the real present is coming soon, and that these are just a backup present. But he said that the headphones were great too, especially when he needs to stay in the hospital for long hours, after surgery or during chemo sessions. He can listen to some soothing music or audiobooks. I hadn't thought about that until he mentioned it—how soon he will start treatment—it's less than a month away. This Christmas may really be the last one. My heart raced thinking about the possibility of losing Daddy. I didn't want to think about it. I got up, reached over to Daddy, and wrapped my arms around him. I said, "I love you" and kissed him on the cheek. I didn't want to let go. He hugged me tightly and kissed me back. "I love you too, princess."

3 Surgery Day

6 January 2017
8:30 a.m.

Daddy is having surgery today. Mummy said I could take a day off school to go to the hospital together. I want to be there when Daddy wakes up from his surgery. He was already admitted into the hospital last night for some check-ups, so I didn't get to kiss him good night. Mummy said we need to go in early if we want to catch him before the surgery, so we left at around half past seven.

On the way to the hospital, I texted Lisa to let her know I wouldn't be at school today and asked her if she could help me collect the assignments for the day. I didn't give her all the details about why I am taking the day off, though—just that it's a family thing. She knows my dad is sick, but she doesn't know much more than that—how serious it is (nor did she even ask). And I don't know if I should tell her or not. When she texted me back with, "Lucky you! I can't believe I have to sit through Mr. Ho blab on and on while you get to stay home!" I felt a knot in my stomach. *I sure am lucky, alright…* But I guess I can't really be mad at her for that, since I haven't told her yet. But telling her now would just make her feel really bad. I mean, when is a good time to tell your friends your dad has cancer, needs surgery and chemo, but may not even survive until the end of the year? When? And how? I don't want people to look at me like I'm some poor girl or feel sorry for me. But I don't want them to be insensitive either or ignore the fact that something like this is happening.

I wish I had a friend I trusted enough to share this kind of thing with, or someone who understands. To be honest, I don't know anyone in my life I feel comfortable talking about this with.

We arrived at the hospital just an hour before the surgery. We are now keeping Daddy company until the nurses come to prep him. I wrapped my arms around Daddy and told him I love him very much. He said he will see me soon and kissed me on the head.

12:25 p.m.

The surgery is very long—almost seven hours. Mummy said I could bring some homework or a book to read while we wait. I started reading *A Little Princess* last week, so I brought that and thought I'd finish reading it today. I just read the last page. Daddy was right about the ending. It is not like the movie at all. I feel very sad that Sara's dad doesn't come back in the end (which I sort of already guessed). I know it's just a story, but it still makes me sad. I have a feeling that Daddy knows he will not make it in the end. The worst part is that we don't know when it's going to be, and that is scary. You hear and read about these kinds of things happening to other people, but you never think that it will ever happen to you. It still feels like I am in a dream sometimes.

There were a few more hours until the surgery was finished so I decided to start writing a new story about me and Daddy. I imagined us with superpowers—super speed and super strength. In the story, there is an earthquake and we go around saving the people who are stuck in the rubble. I like writing stories where we do things that we would never be able to do in real life. It makes me happy to imagine and live in a fantasy, if only for a little while. Last week, I wrote a story about us rock climbing to the top of the mountain and watching the beautiful sunset together. Daddy said that he misses watching the sunset with me and I told him that we will be watching the sunset together very soon.

3:45 p.m.

The surgery is finally over. We watched the nurses wheel Daddy back to his room and the doctors told us that everything went smoothly and that he is okay. He is still under the anesthesia but will wake up soon. They said they have removed the tumours in the pancreas and reconstructed and reattached a bunch of organs in his digestive system. Everything sounds so technical and scientific, and quite scary. I am just happy to hear that he is okay. The nurses hooked him up to some machines to monitor his vitals and put some tubes in his nose to help him breathe.

Then they attached something in his hand for a drip that goes directly into his vein. The nurse explained it's used for giving him medicine for the pain as well as nutrients because he cannot eat any solid food for a few days.

Daddy looks very tired, but he looks kind of peaceful, too. It almost looks like his mouth is curving upwards into a smile. Mummy and I are waiting beside his bed for him to wake up.

I have been praying every day for the last two months now. I really hope that God is listening. *Can you hear me, God?*

5:20 p.m.

Daddy finally woke up, just twenty minutes ago. I walked over and gave him a gentle hug and kiss on his cheek. His face lit up and he smiled at me. Tears started falling down my cheek, but Daddy wiped them away and told me not to cry. "I'm fine, see?" He lifted his right arm up, made a fist and pretended to flex his bicep. "Oh, I'm happy to see you are okay, Daddy! These are happy tears," I said and smiled. I am so relieved that he is okay. He didn't stay awake for too long; he fell asleep again after a few minutes. That surgery sure took a lot out of him. Mummy and I are tired, too. After a short while, she fell asleep as well. Now, I think it's my turn…

4　Preparing for Chemo

16 February 2017
8:00 p.m.

It's been a month since the surgery and Daddy is still recovering. It was a really big surgery and the scar is quite long. I have to be very careful and gentle if I want to hug him, which is all the time. Sometimes Daddy likes it when I hug him, but other times he asks me not to because it hurts.

The doctors want to make sure his wounds are healed and that he is strong enough before they start the chemo, so he will go in for a check- up tomorrow to see if he is ready. The medicine from the chemo would kill a lot of the cancer cells in his body—including some of the good cells. And the side effects can be quite bad as well, like nausea, vomiting, hair loss… I don't know why a medicine would make you sicker than you already are. Daddy didn't want to do it at first, but the doctors said it was his best chance to extend his life for a few more months, but still, it was no guarantee. (Sometimes, I wonder if doctors themselves would want to do all of these treatments that they are giving to their patients.)

I read online that less than 5% actually survive pancreatic cancer in the first five years, even with treatment. So, all of this could be for nothing. And after five years, the cancer could come back again or spread to other organs in the body. Daddy said he would try it just once and then decide if he wants to continue the treatment. I know it is a very tough decision to make. I just don't want to see Daddy in pain. I don't know what I can do. I squeezed my hands together and closed my eyes. I tried really hard to concentrate this time. *Can you hear me, God? Why aren't you doing anything?*

5　First Chemo Session

24 February 2017
9:30 p.m.

Daddy had his first chemo session this morning while I was at school. I came home straight from school to see him. Mummy said he had been sleeping since they came home after lunch. She said he seemed okay and to just let him rest a bit longer until it was time for dinner. But at dinner time, Daddy didn't want to eat anything and only had some soup.

He just wanted to sleep. I can't sleep, though. I keep thinking about the side effects, and if Daddy will experience any of those soon.

Also, at school today, Lisa asked me why I have been so down lately. I didn't really feel like talking about it, so I just said it was nothing. I finished my lunch quickly and went to the library to be alone. I felt so tired and nodded off while reading a book on the desk. Ms Lee, the librarian, had to wake me up so I wouldn't be late for class. I could barely concentrate during math, either. All I heard from Mr. Woo was something about 'a, b, c.' What do these letters have to do with math anyway? When he asked me a question, I just made an excuse that I needed to use the bathroom and didn't return until ten minutes later. Then the bell rang. Mr. Woo asked me if something was wrong. I said I didn't sleep well the night before and just needed a good night's sleep. He didn't grill me anymore after that. Phew! It's not like I was lying. I really didn't sleep well, and afternoon lessons are the worst! No one can concentrate well after lunch. Thank God it's Saturday tomorrow and I can catch up on my sleep.

6   Side Effects of Chemo

26 February 2017
5:00 p.m.

I went to church this morning with Grandpa and Grandma. I went to Sunday School while they went to the service. Mummy has to stay home to look after Daddy every day now, but she doesn't want me to miss out on church, so she asked Grandpa and Grandma to take me. She says it's important to stay connected to God and to have faith and keep praying—and I have been—every day.

After our group discussion time, my teacher, Ms. Young, came to talk to me. She said she had noticed "a change in my behaviour lately." She also spoke to Grandma briefly during worship time this morning. She said she knows and understands how tough it is to see Daddy go through this. I felt relieved that she knows now, in a way. We talked for a while and I told her about some of the things I was worried about, and how I was not sleeping well, and that Daddy had surgery and chemo for the first time. She prayed for me and Daddy and told me that I can talk to her any time. She even gave me her phone number and email address. I feel a bit better that there is someone I can talk to now.

We came back home at around 3:00 p.m. When I walked in, Mummy said I needed to keep quiet. She left the door to their room open in case Daddy needed anything. He's been resting most of the day. I tip-toed quietly to take a quick peek at him. His eyes were closed, and he seemed to be sleeping soundly, so I went back to the living room.

About an hour later, I heard Daddy call out to us, "Help! I'm going to be sick!" Mummy was busy frying something in the kitchen, so she quickly handed a wash basin to me and told me to give it to Daddy. I rushed down the hall and into his room with it and saw Daddy bent over on the edge of the bed, hugging his tummy. He looked like he was in a lot of pain. He grabbed the basin from my hands and told me to turn around. I turned around but I could still hear everything—the bubbling gurgling sound his throat made when it all overflowed into his mouth, the moment everything hit the bottom of the basin, his painful groans and gasps for air. I stood there, frozen. I wanted to cover my ears, but I didn't want him to see me like that. I wanted to be brave and turn around, but I was afraid of showing him the scared look I had on my face. I wanted to rush out to Mummy, but I didn't want to leave him. Instead, I grabbed his face towel and put it under hot water to make it warm. He had stopped vomiting, but he looked like he had just run a marathon, with flushed cheeks, beads of sweat on his forehead, and his mouth wide open, still gasping for air. He let out a few coughs and spit some of his saliva into the basin. I handed the towel to him and his arm raised up shakily to take it from me. He rubbed the towel across his mouth and face while his whole body shivered. I gave him a glass of water to rinse out his mouth.

Mummy finally came in. She took the basin from Daddy and emptied it into the toilet. She told me to sit with Daddy while she cleaned everything up. I pulled a blanket over Daddy's shoulders and gave him a gentle hug.

After a few minutes, Daddy said, "I feel much better now." He put his arms around my shoulders and squeezed me tightly. "Sorry you had to see that. I hope I didn't scare you, sweetheart."

"It's okay, Daddy. I wasn't scared," I lied. I was a little scared, but it started last night already. I had heard those same sounds coming from their room after midnight. I didn't tell him, though. I just feel really sorry for Daddy that he has to go through this. It hurts my heart. I don't even know how to describe the feeling. It took me a long time to fall back asleep after that.

Mummy came over and sat down on the other side next to Daddy. "Let's pray together for Daddy," she said. When Mummy started praying, I couldn't really hear what she was saying, so I started praying silently in my heart and asked God to end Daddy's pain and suffering. Then, I imagined me and Daddy going on adventures around the world together and seeing his healthy face smiling back at me, just like in my stories.

After Mummy said "Amen," Daddy let out a sigh and said quietly under his breath, "I don't want to do anymore chemo."

"Okay," was all Mummy said.

7   Changes and Staycation

17 March 2017
12:50 p.m.

It's been a pretty crazy couple of weeks. Today is a pretty big day, though, but I need explain what happened over the last week.

I finally decided to tell Lisa about Daddy. Ms. Young told me that I should open up and share with my friends about what is happening. She said it is not good for me to keep everything to myself and it is important that I have friends who can be there for me. Lisa is probably my closest friend at school, but we mostly talk about silly and funny things and hardly ever talk about the sad or bad things. I was a bit nervous about telling her at first, but afterwards, I felt relieved that I did. She gave me a big hug and said that she was sorry I had to go through all that alone for the last few months. She said her uncle also had cancer two years ago and passed away, so she can sort of understand what it's like. She said she felt bad about that text now and wished I had told her earlier so she could have been there for me. I told her that it was okay, and it was silly of me to keep it from her. I'm glad we can talk openly like this now. Mummy also spoke to my teachers at school because I may need to take some days off school once in a while. They were all very understanding and kind. Ms. Lau, my class teacher, even had a chat with me at lunch break and told me I could talk to her any time if I needed. It felt so much better to finally talk to others (who aren't Mummy or Daddy) about it.

Surprisingly, I was finally able to have a good night's sleep without waking up in the middle of the night. I realised I'd need more energy and time to spend with Daddy and started to plan and rearrange my schedule. I went to bed earlier and woke up earlier. I finished most—if not all—of my homework in the library before I got home. I helped Mummy with more chores at home so she could take care of Daddy. Daddy also said he didn't want me to lose track at school and not be able to keep up with my studies and assignments because of him. He had always emphasised how important it is to study and work hard at school so I could have a good future. I don't want to let him down and have him think that it's his fault if I don't do well. It's my responsibility to work hard. I had completely changed my sleep and study habits and even my mood improved a little.

Actually, Daddy seems to be getting better as well! Since he isn't doing chemo anymore, he doesn't have much nausea or vomiting. He has started to lose some hair, though, so I bought him a new beanie to wear. He seems to have a slightly better appetite, so Mummy's been making more of his favourite foods, like spaghetti bolognese, chicken wings, and salmon (although he then said he couldn't stand the fishy smell anymore). Daddy even has a bit more energy back, so we have been going on short walks together every day for a week. He said he feels his muscles are getting stronger. I think God is finally listening to my prayers!

Last Saturday, Mummy said that we should go on a short family trip together, now that Daddy has his energy back. Daddy loved that idea and said that as long as we are together, it doesn't matter where we go. We decided to go to the Noah's Ark Hotel and Resort. Daddy has always loved going to the beach and there is a beautiful beach there right next to the hotel. We will be going there right after school today. Mummy told me to make sure I finish all my homework and assignments during breaks and recesses so I can enjoy the time. Mummy also asked

Ms. Lau for permission for me to take Monday and Tuesday off as well, so she gave me the work for those days ahead of time. I've been staying in the classroom or going to the library every break and sneaking time in between lessons all week to finish. I got everything done by lunchtime today! I am super excited and can't wait to go to Noah's Ark!

6:00 pm.

It was around 5:00 p.m. when we arrived and there was still a bit of sun. I asked if we could go to the beach to watch the sunset before going to our room. Daddy was even more excited than I was! We took our shoes off and walked out on the sand. Daddy almost lost his balance because the sand was so soft! Mummy and I each took one of Daddy's arms and guided him down until we found the perfect spot to watch the sunset. We sat down on the sand, stretched out our legs, and breathed in the warm misty air. Daddy started humming a random tune while we admired the breath-taking view in front of us. We just sat there, listening to Daddy's humming, while we watched the orange sun disappear behind the mountains. I couldn't stop grinning from ear to ear! I looked over at Daddy—his eyes were closed but he had the biggest smile on his face. He was still humming the tune. I hooked my arm around his, rested my head on his shoulder, and hummed along with him. Daddy whispered quietly into my ear, "I will always love you, no matter what happens."

21 March 2017
9:30 a.m.

I can't believe how quickly the last few days flew by. We've spent an hour each morning walking on the beach and singing hymns together after breakfast. Then we had some quiet time praying or reading or just lying on the sand, soaking in the sunshine. We also had long chats and played some card games together. Most of the time, we were very happy and cheerful, but yesterday morning, Daddy got a bit angry. I still don't really know what happened. When I woke up, I heard Mummy and Daddy arguing. Mummy started crying because Daddy was yelling at her, so I walked over to give Mummy a hug, but that seemed to upset Daddy even more. I didn't know what to do. I'd never seen Daddy like this before. I started crying too, and that's when Daddy walked out of the room. Mummy hugged me and said that Daddy was just having a bad day.

Daddy came back an hour later, carrying a box of cupcakes. He said that he was sorry for yelling and scaring us. He said he had been feeling a lot of anger lately and didn't know how to release it. He wasn't really angry at us, but he just needed to let it out. Daddy looked really sad then and had tears in his eyes. He asked if we would forgive him. Mummy and I both went up to Daddy and gave him a hug, then Daddy broke down in tears on Mummy's shoulders. We held on to each other for a long time and let all our tears out.

11:30 a.m.

When it was time to leave, just as we were rolling our suitcases out, I asked Daddy if there was anything he still wanted to do. Daddy paused for a few seconds, then said, "I have done everything I've ever wanted to do already. And I have everything I need in this world. I have no regrets."

When we got to the lobby, he added, "I can't wait to go home!"

24

8 Good Days and Bad Days

23 April 2017
8:00 p.m.

Daddy has good days and bad days. After that day at Noah's Ark Hotel, I noticed Daddy's mood changes more and more. He doesn't yell like he did that time, but he has this grumpy look on his face and groans when he doesn't like something. Mummy and I have gotten used to it and we remind each other that Daddy is just having a bad day and he will be better soon. His bad moods usually just last a couple of hours, and afterwards, he sometimes pretends like nothing is wrong or sometimes he apologises. It was a bit tough at first, and I didn't really understand why he was having these bad moods. But then I thought about what it must be like for him, having cancer, this pain and nauseous feeling all the time, not being able to eat what you want, and the uncertainty of it all. Of course, anyone would have bad moods in this situation. Even though it's not nice to see him like this, I would rather see him in a bad mood than not see him at all.

On his good days, we can talk about anything. Sometimes he asks me to read to him. Sometimes we listen to music and sing along together. Sometimes we watch old movies, like we used to every weekend And sometimes, we just sit together and don't need to say anything. This might sound weird, but I actually quite like just listening to the sound of Daddy's breathing, and feeling his chest move up and down.

9 Good Things Can Come from Bad Things

14 May 2017
9:20 p.m.

Today at church I had a long talk with Ms. Young after Sunday School I asked her if Daddy was sick because I hadn't been a very good girl and always forgot to pray, because Daddy has always been a good man and doesn't deserve this suffering. She said that God is not cruel; He's a good God. Daddy's illness is not a punishment for my wrongdoings either. There also aren't any truly good people in the world, except Jesus. We are all sinners in a fallen world. That is why there is suffering—we can't avoid it. But she said that suffering is only for a little while and our time in this world is limited.

It wasn't an easy thing to hear and I didn't fully understand it at first. She said that even though God allows bad things to happen, He uses those bad things for good. "We know that in all things God works for the good of those who love him…" (Romans 8:28). We may not understand God's reasons for our suffering right now, and we can't see what good can come out of it yet, but we need to trust Him and remember that He is always good. Someday, we will be blessed in ways we'd never imagined.

Ms. Young suggested that I write down some of the good things that have happened over the last few months and to continue doing that every day. When I look back at it later, I will be able to see how God used the bad things for good. At first, I got a bit angry at her when she said that. It didn't make a lot of sense to me—what good can come from Daddy suffering and possibly dying? When I got home, I sat down and thought for a long time. I thought back to the last few months...

1. I got to spend more time with Daddy, and he doesn't have to work long hours anymore.
2. We spent time as a family together at Noah's Ark and watched the sunset on the beach.
3. My friendship with Lisa became closer since I opened up to her about Daddy.
4. I have been better at managing my time and finishing all my work faster.
5. I started helping Mummy more and learned how to do different chores. I even learned how to make soup and porridge for Daddy.
6. I can talk to Daddy a lot more freely and openly than before and I tell him that I love him every day now.

After writing down the list, I could see that I have changed a lot over the last few months. God allowed the bad things to happen to help us grow stronger, learn how to take good care of each other, and appreciate each other more.

10 You Just Need to Have Faith

31 May 2017
8:00 p.m.

Daddy is getting weaker and weaker now. He still feels pain when he eats, and he cannot sleep very well. He has lost a lot of weight. I thought things were improving for him, but it seems that the cancer cells are growing and spreading because he stopped the treatments. It makes me sad to see him like this. Every day after school, I come straight home to cheer him up. I show him what I have done at school and sometimes read the stories I have written to him.

Today I wrote a new story about Daddy and me at the circus. We perform tricks and tame the lions. The audience cheers for us, and we are very excited and proud! Daddy really likes the story. He always said that even though he can't do any of those things with me now, it makes him happy to imagine them when he listens to me describe them. I told him that when he gets better, we can do some of those things (though I'm not sure about taming the lions!). Before, Daddy would smile and say, "Okay!" but today, Daddy looked at me with tears in his eyes and said that he would not get better.

"But I have been praying for you, Daddy. God will make you better." Daddy held my hands in his and said, "If God makes me better, I will be very grateful and happy that I can spend more time with you and Mummy. But if God doesn't make me better, that means that He needs me in Heaven with Him. And I will be very grateful and happy about that too. No matter what happens, I will be happy and peaceful because God knows what is best for you and me."

I have known for a while that Daddy might not make it but hearing him say it out loud makes it feel very real. I suddenly felt warm tears well up in my eyes. I didn't want him to see me like that, but I just couldn't hold them back anymore. "I don't want you to go, Daddy!" I cried.

"I will always be with you, in here," he said, pointing to my heart. "Even if my body is not here, I will still live on in your heart. And you don't need to see me to talk to me, you know. You can talk to me whenever you want, wherever you are, if you keep me in your heart."

"Will you still be able to hear me?" I asked.

"Of course! You may not always hear *me*, but I will always be able to hear you, and even see you from Heaven. Heaven will give me special powers. Can you promise to keep talking to me and telling me your stories? And I promise that I will always listen."

"Yes! I promise!" I said. "But how will I know if you can hear me?"

Daddy thought for a moment and replied, "You just need to have faith. Think of me when you see something beautiful—like a flower, a rainbow, or a butterfly—I will be there. Even when you just close your eyes and think of me, I will be there. It's just like when you pray to God. You may never see or hear Him, but you have faith that He is watching over you and listening to your prayers. So, you just need to have faith, okay?"

I nodded and I climbed onto Daddy's bed to give him a big hug. He squeezed me tightly and kissed my forehead.

"Are you scared, Daddy?" I asked.

"I was—maybe a few months ago. But I'm not anymore. I can't wait to go home."

"You *are* home!" I said, confused.

"This is not our real home. Our *real* home is with God in Heaven," he said. "I can't wait! And one day, a long, long, loooong time from now, we will see each other again!"

11 Father's Day

18 June 2017
3:30 p.m.

A lot of Daddy's friends came to visit him this week. The doctors told us that he doesn't have much time left. Daddy is actu-ally staying in the hospice now, where the doctors and nurses can check on him regularly and monitor his heartbeat and blood pressure. Mummy has been staying with him in his room for the last two nights. I came to visit him after school for a few hours yesterday and the day before, and then went home with Grandma and Grandpa after dinner. Today is Sunday, so I can spend all day with him here now. It's also Father's Day! I wrote a poem for Daddy yesterday. I worked really hard on it. I handed the poem to Daddy when I came in after breakfast and he asked me to read it to him.

The poem goes like this:

> Thank you so much for being my Daddy.
> You always know how to make me happy.
> You give me a hug when I'm feeling sad,
> Even thought I sometimes make you mad,
> And forget to say, "Thank you" or "I love you."

But you still love me, no matter what I do.
I want you to know, Daddy—I will always love you!

Daddy said he really likes the poem and wants me to read it to him every day.

Daddy's room has a gorgeous view of the garden outside and he said he wanted to go and see it before the sun was gone, so we wheeled him outside to enjoy the sunset. We even saw some butterflies flying around the flowers in the garden. We could hear the birds chirping and singing. Daddy even started humming along! I saw some little white flowers on the ground and walked over to pick them up. I put one in my hair, like Daddy used to do when I was small. He smiled and said I looked beautiful! I gave him the other flowers and lifted them up to his nose so he could smell them. He took a deep breath in and said that he had not smelled anything so lovely for a long time.

We wheeled Daddy back into his room after the sun disappeared, and a little blue butterfly followed us all the way inside! "I wish I could be just like that butterfly," he said. "I can enjoy the warm sunshine and smell lovely flowers all day long! I can even fly wherever I want!"

12 One Wish

20 June 2017
8:50 p.m.

I talked to Daddy for a long time after school today. I asked him what he liked most about me and Mummy. He said he cannot think of just one thing because he loves everything about us—even the silly things—like when I hid in the bathroom for two hours to read so no one would disturb me, or when Mummy wore two different coloured socks to dinner at a fancy restaurant (Mummy's face turned bright red when he mentioned that!). He said those things actually made him love us even more!

Then Mummy asked Daddy, "If you could have one wish, what would it be?" Daddy thought for a moment and said, "I wish to go home." There was that word again—home. After he explained it to me last time, I started getting a strange feeling. It's difficult to describe it, though. I know that Daddy may leave here at any time, and at first, I was really sad and angry, and even a bit scared. But when he told me that he couldn't wait to go home to Heaven, even though it meant he would not be with us anymore, I didn't feel angry or scared. I still feel sad, but not so sad I want to cry all the time, like I did before. I feel... calmer, more peaceful. I thought back to the first three months when I started asking God to heal Daddy and make him better, and nothing seemed to be working. Since May, when I started making a list of the good things that happened, I started saying prayers to thank God instead. He has blessed me, Daddy, and Mummy in so many other ways and gave us things we didn't know we needed. He really does know what is best for us. It's not that I no longer want Daddy to get better, I still really hope that God will perform some kind of miracle, but I know that it's not up to me or Mummy or the doctors or even Daddy. Daddy has been trying to tell me that, too. I was surprised when he said that he wasn't scared anymore. Hearing him say that made me less scared, too.

This week, there are three things that I am thankful for:

1. Daddy is looking happier and smiling these last few days. He stopped having the bad moods. It was like he was a different person!
2. Daddy blessed a lot of people around him through his uplifting spirit and cheerful smiles. Some of the friends who came to visit him were surprised to see him looking so cheerful, and said they felt encouraged by him. The doctor and nurses also said the same thing and always looked forward to seeing him! Whenever I look at Daddy now, I can't help but smile—just like him.
3. We were able to share so much with each other over these last few weeks and months, something we had never done before. We talked about the good and bad times and apologised for the times we made each other angry. We forgave each other.

13 Waiting

21 June 2017
9:30 p.m.

Today has been a strange day. After visiting Daddy, I came home feeling like I was floating, somehow. There is still a part of me that feels like this is all a dream, that it's not real. It's like I'm living in a movie that I'm also watching at the same time. I see all the things that are happening before my eyes, and a lot of the times, the things don't seem to register or make sense to me until a few hours later or the next day. I sometimes start to wonder—did that really happen? Looking back at what I've recorded in the last few months, I can see that so much has happened and changed in my life, and with Daddy and Mummy. It feels like I'm living a completely different life than I was six months ago.

The last few days are just starting to sink in, though. I realised how close we are to the end, and for the last few days, I started waiting. What is most unbearable is the uncertain feeling of "when?" Each day begins with the question: *Will it be today?* and ends with a sigh of relief, but then

I wonder: *What if it's tomorrow?* I'm waiting and waiting each day—for my dad to die. It is the worst feeling in the world. How many more days will be like this? How much longer do I need to wait (for something I don't want to happen)? I can't take it anymore. Yet, I don't want it to end.

14 The Last Day

22 June 2017
4:45 p.m.

Daddy has been sleeping for a long time since yesterday. He didn't even wake up to eat or drink. The doctor said we should let him rest because he is very tired and there is nothing they can do anymore. I am sad that I can't do anything to help Daddy. Mummy said that I should keep talking to him and telling him my stories. I didn't really know what to say so I took out my stories and read them to him again. I read the Father's Day poem to him as well.

I sat quietly next to Mummy when all the stories were finished. Mummy started sobbing, so I gave her a hug and kissed her on the cheek. "God needs Daddy in Heaven now. Daddy says that he will be happy there." I tried to comfort Mummy, but it didn't help.

10:30 p.m.

Daddy's breathing is heavy and slow now. Each breath sounds painful for him. We held his hands tightly and prayed together. Then I leaned closer to Daddy and whispered in his ear, "Can you hear me, Daddy? We love you so much. You don't have to worry about us. You can go peacefully to Heaven now. God is waiting for you." It really hurt my heart to say that. I don't want to see Daddy go but it's not good to keep him here like this.

All the waiting over the last few days doesn't compare to today. We've been here for eight hours but it feels like it's stretching to days. I started to count the seconds between each of his breaths. They started getting longer and further apart. My eyes are tired and strained from crying; I am barely keeping them open. I started watching his chest rise up and down. I didn't want to miss a single breath. Each drop of his chest seemed to make my eyelids heavier and heavier, though. Mummy told me to lie down to take a rest. I didn't really want to, but I guess I can close my eyes and continue to listen to the sound of Daddy's breathing.

15 Daddy's Home

23 June 2017
12:40 a.m.

I suddenly woke up when I heard Mummy moving around. When I open-
-ed my eyes, I saw her kneeling on the ground with her head on
Daddy's bed, holding his hands. *Oh, no!* I walked slowly towards the bed.
My eyes narrowed and focused on Daddy's chest. *Move, come on.* I held
my own breath, waiting for him. I started to count. Five seconds went by.
Ten. Nothing. The room was silent. He was completely still.

"Can you hear me, Daddy? I love you! Please come back!" I cried.

"It's okay, sweetie," Mummy said. "Daddy's home now." I held on to
Mummy as my eyes filled with tears. *I can't believe it! It hurts so much!* I
could hardly breathe! Mummy picked me up, carried me out of the room
and laid me down on the sofa in the waiting room. She pulled a blanket
over me and then called a nurse to come.

8:05 a.m.

When I woke up, I saw Mummy sleeping beside me. I walked quietly into Daddy's room and saw that his bed was empty. Mummy came up behind me and wrapped her arms around me. We cried and cried until no more tears would come out.

Mummy took me home and we saw Grandma was already there. She had made breakfast for us. Mummy and I sat down and ate quietly together. Grandma broke the silence and said, "Your daddy was a wonderful man. We will all miss him very much."

I went to my room after finishing breakfast and crashed down onto my bed. My whole body ached, and my heart felt like it was breaking. Even though I knew this would happen, I didn't expect it to hurt so much. It hurts deep inside. It's like there is a hole in my heart and the hole is getting bigger and bigger. I couldn't hold back my tears and I cried into my pillow to muffle the sound.

16 Celebration of Life

12 July 2017
4:00 p.m.

Today is Daddy's memorial service. Mummy said we should call it "A Celebration of Life" because we want to remember all the good things Daddy did and all the people who love and remember Daddy should share the happy moments and memories of him. I share about the time Daddy took me swimming and we raced to the other side of the pool but ended up getting there at the same time, when he told us silly jokes and we couldn't stop laughing until our tummies ached, the time he told me to dream big and follow my dreams and that he would be proud of me no matter what, and how much I enjoyed reading him all the stories about our silly adventures together.

I listened to other people's stories about Daddy too. They said he was very kind and helpful. Daddy always remembered what they had told him because he was a very good listener. They never got bored talking to him. I am so happy and proud to have such a wonderful daddy.

17 Can You Hear Me, Daddy?

2 January 2018
5:30 p.m.

Today is Daddy's birthday. Even though he is no longer here with us, we will still celebrate his birthday. Mummy and I went to his resting place to visit him. I wrote another story for Daddy, so I brought it with me. Mummy got some flowers. I looked at Daddy's picture and smiled. I said quietly, "Sometimes I still feel sad that you are not here anymore. But I remember that you said I can talk to you whenever and wherever I want and that makes me feel a lot better. I will always miss you. I will always love you… Can you hear me, Daddy?" I still wasn't really sure if Daddy could hear me. He said that I needed to have faith and to think of him. I wondered if he was there.

Mummy held my hand and we prayed together. Then, she said to me, "It's okay to feel sad, darling. I feel sad too, sometimes. And even cry. But I always remember the happy moments we had with Daddy and I thank God for every day that he was with us—good days and bad days—and then I am not so sad anymore."

I took out the story that was folded in my pants pocket and started reading it while Mummy laid the flowers down for Daddy.

Then, I saw a beautiful blue butterfly fly over and land on the flowers! Mummy held my hand tightly and we watched the butterfly flutter around the flowers. It didn't fly away; it stayed there for a long time. I started thinking of Daddy. "Are you here, Daddy? Can you hear me?" The butterfly got up, flew towards me, then landed on my shoulder! Mummy started to smile and laugh! "I think he can!"

"I promise, Daddy!" I said. Then the butterfly flew over to Mummy. "I promise!" she said.

"Heaven really does give you special powers!" I said. "I will always love you, Daddy. You will always be with me. I promise to keep you in my heart and talk to you every day. I know you can hear me now!"

"I think you should finish reading your story. Daddy would love to hear it."

I continued to read as the butterfly fluttered around us. When I finished reading, we watched and waited until it flew away.

Acknowledgments

This book is dedicated to my dad, Charles—the inspiration for this book—whom I would have loved to thank in person, but I know he is watching me right now from Heaven, with the brightest and biggest smile on his face! I remember when I first told him that I wanted to write a book, he simply said, "Go for it!" Without a moment's hesitation. I regret not writing those stories sooner for him to read. Dad, I promise to read them to you every day from now on!

I want to thank my mum, Jennifer, for always taking care of me and encouraging me to do things I never thought I could do. And thank you for reminding me what it means to have faith in God. Thank you to my brother, Daniel, who has inspired me to chase after my dreams. Seeing you make movies all on your own makes me want to push myself more and more every day.

I want to thank all my brothers and sisters from my church, Island ECC in Hong Kong (too many to name!), for supporting me, praying for me, and encouraging me to make good use of my gifts and talents, to make my dream a reality and share my testimony with others.

Thank you to those I have bugged these last few months over messages and emails about reading and reviewing my writing, and giving me feedback, suggestions and ideas to keep making it better. (You know who you are!)

Thank you to my editor and coach, Marcy Pusey, for your encouraging feedback and meticulous efforts in editing my manuscript! Thank you for giving me the confidence boosts I needed to push forward to the finish line.

Thank you also to the Self-Publishing School Community and the #WritingCommunity across different platforms, and all the other kind and helpful individuals whom I've connected with since I started writing, for all your wonderful support and feedback! Even though I had never met any of you before, you have become my new family and I have learned so much from you all!

Last but not least, I want to thank God, who has been with me through it all. He has given me hope, joy, and peace when I was grieving and mourning. I was lost for so long, but He came after me and never gave up on me. None of this would have been possible without Him!

About the Author

Y. Y. Chan was born in Hong Kong but grew up in sunny Brisbane, Australia, where she had Christmas during summer. She returned to Hong Kong to teach English after graduating from university with First Class Honours. She has an M.A. In English Language Teaching, and has been teaching English for over ten years.

When her father passed away, she took a break from teaching to travel, read, and write. She now tutors English and works freelance for different educational institutes.

Her best writing comes out late at night when everyone else is asleep. When she is not writing or teaching, she is either reading or looking for more books to add to her overflowing bookshelf. Her debut picture book, *Can You Hear Me, Daddy?* is the winner of the Royal Dragonfly Book Award.

To see news and updates on her work, go to www.yychani.com to subscribe. You can also send an email to chanyyi86@gmail.com to let her know what you think of the book!

Praise for *Can You Hear Me?*

Readers' Favorite International Book Award
Gold Medal Winner
(Children - Religious Theme)

"This is a powerful story that will help readers of all ages deal with their grief. Told with care and compassion."

– Emily-Jane Hills, Readers' Favorite

"...[This] is a poignant story of hope and loss. Written like a diary, this book is perfect for children experiencing and who have recently experienced the loss of a loved one..."

– Alyssa Elmore, Reader's Favorite

"This is a must-read for anyone who is going through the journey of cancer... As an Emotional Intelligence Coach, I will definitely use this with my clients who are not equipped yet to navigate through the emotion of fear... I highly recommend this book for anyone that is preparing, going through, or has experienced loss in their life–parents and children alike!"

– Dr. Renea Skelton

"...There aren't enough gold stars to give it and there aren't enough adjectives in the English language to applaud it. This book is the kind of book you're happy to have read and afterwards, you will keep it around in case anyone else you know might need it...Truly inspirational."

– James Roberts, Amazon Reviewer

Discussion Questions

1. Renee wondered if God was punishing her for her bad behavior and forgetting to pray. Have you ever felt like this? What happened?

2. Why do you think her daddy wanted her to write another story for him as a Christmas present?

3. Her daddy gave A Little Princess (by Frances Hodgson Burnett) to her as a Christmas present. Why did he choose this book? How is this book significant to the rest of the story? (Have you read this book before?)

4. Renee wondered if God was listening to her prayers, whether other people were praying hard enough, and if her daddy was praying to get better himself. Does God always answer your prayers? If He doesn't, does that mean He isn't listening? Why do you think God didn't make her daddy better after all her prayers?

5. How did things change after Renee started talking to Ms. Young and Lisa? Why is it important to talk to others about what you are going through?

6. Ms. Young told Renee that "good things can come from bad things." Do you remember any good things that came from a bad situation in your past experience? What were they?

7. How did faith help Renee cope with the loss of her dad?

Author's Note

I wrote this story after grieving the loss of my own father to pancreatic cancer in 2017. I felt immense pain and sorrow as an adult and could not imagine how it would have felt if I had been younger. Yet, these inevitable events can occur to anyone at any time, without warning. During the editing of this book, my beloved grandmother passed away peacefully on 9th April 2020. She had just turned 95 years old. Even though we knew this day would come, it was still a shock when it did. It was expected, yet unexpected—it's a very strange feeling. I always just expected to see her again, not realising how fleeting those moments were. And just because it has happened before, it doesn't hurt any less when it happens again.

Everyone experiences grief a little differently. Each loss is different, and the process of grief and mourning are also different. There isn't a one-size-fits-all model for everyone. Each time is a new and different journey. Our moods and feelings can change suddenly within seconds; it's unpredictable and we can't control them. The stages of grief are not linear, either. I also don't believe that it will ever completely end, though it does get easier as time goes on. There will also be special days and occasions each year where the memory will bring back a little bit of the pain, but that's okay. Dwell in those moments and remember the good times you had together. But don't feel bad about forgetting either.

I hope this story helps children of all ages, even adults and parents, understand loss, to process their own grief and emotions, rather than suppress them, and to communicate them in a healthy way with people they can trust.

Though the events in this story are mostly fictional, the feelings and emotions portrayed are very real. This was a difficult story to write and may also be difficult and heavy to read. However, I believe that we need to have open and honest discussions about these difficult topics early to make the grieving journey a little easier, whenever that time comes.

Faith is a big part of this story because this was what got me through that difficult time. I had strayed far away from God before my dad got sick, and it took losing my dad for me to realise how much I really needed God in my life. Although I had felt immense pain deep in my heart, I also experienced great joy when I reconnected with God. He gave me hope and peace, knowing that death is not the end, but the beginning of an eternity with Him—when we are finally home. It is okay to feel sadness and pain, and these feelings, like sickness and death, are all an inevitable part of life. But no one has to suffer through it all alone, nor will our sufferings last forever.

"...our present sufferings are not worth comparing with the glory that will be revealed in us" (Romans 8:18).

—Y.Y. Chan

Can you help?

Thank you for reading my book! I really hope you enjoyed it! I hope to keep spreading the message of hope and joy–even in times of grief and sorrow, and I need your help to keep it going–to be the light in the darkness. I would love it if you could leave an honest review on whichever platform you found my book. This helps to get the book noticed so more people can get a chance to see it and pass the message on! Every review counts and it makes my day to read your honest feedback, shared experiences, and words of encouragement! Feel free to share this story with your friends and family, or anyone whom you think would benefit from it.

As a thank you for buying, reading and reviewing this book, a special gift is waiting for you: a Discussion & Reflection Guide. You can claim your gift by emailing me directly at chanyyi86@gmail.com, and letting me know you have read the book and what you thought! This Discussion & Reflection Guide can be used by social workers, teachers in classrooms, small group leaders and counsellors in church ministries or hospitals, or just as a self-reflection guide for personal use.

Don't forget to subscribe to my mailing list! Sign up here https://www.subscribepage.com/yychani for other special offers and freebies, and to keep up-to-date about the other projects and books I am working on!

There is also a picture book version of this story, *Can You Hear Me, Daddy?* which is full of beautiful illustrations and a simplified storyline. Feel free to check it out too! Visit https://bit.ly/yychan-cyhmd for more details.

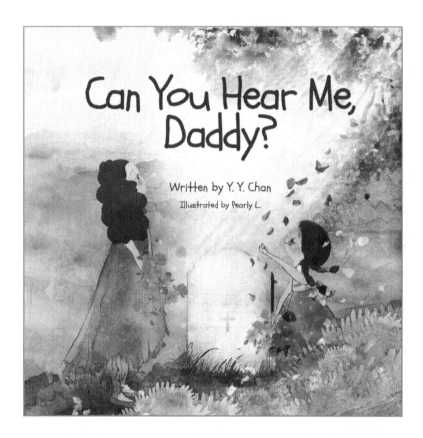

Made in the USA
Middletown, DE
02 October 2021